# Chatter *with* the Angels

## An Illustrated Songbook for Children

G-4900
F0011 13

# Chatter with the Angels

## An Illustrated Songbook for Children

Compiled and edited by
Linda S. Richer and Anita Stoltzfus Breckbill

Illustrated by Susan Graber Hunsberger

Original and edited accompaniments by Robert N. Roth

GIA Publications, Inc.

Chicago

*The artwork was done on Bienfang Drawing Bristol*
*using mostly Prismacolor pencils, and a touch of acrylic paint.*
*The text type is Times.*
*The display type is Delphin I.*

*Music engraved by Beverly Thiege*

*Music editing and book layout by Jeffry Mickus*

*ISBN # 1-579999-082-7*

*1 2 3 4 5 6 7 8 9 10 11 12 13 14 15 16 17 18 19*

DEDICATED TO THE CHILDREN IN OUR LIVES

Tara and Patrick
Hannah and Ben
Evelyn
Abigail, Sunjay, and Stephanos

# Contents

# Introduction

A long search for an illustrated songbook to use with our children, ages three to ten, led us to the idea of compiling our own. Our goal was to introduce our children to Christian songs that they would find enjoyable, meaningful, and enduring. These qualities emerge in three ways: text, tune and illustration.

1. Text: Our chosen texts portray God as a gentle, loving God who cares for us and as a great and creative force in our world. They tell of the beauty and power of nature and of the changing seasons of the year. The songbook includes texts that undergird the church year along with texts that illustrate Bible stories and characters children know. Simple and direct language, as well as inclusive language to refer to people and to God, were important considerations in our process of selecting and editing.

2. Tune: The tunes and melodies represent a wide variety of time periods, styles, and cultures. Hymns and songs of folk origins are particularly well matched to children's voices because of the manageable musical intervals, vocal ranges, and musical forms. The variety of cultures represented also emphasizes that God's message is meant for all people, a major theme of this book.

3. Illustration: Noting that memories are made through both the eye and the ear, our collection strives to stimulate children's imaginations through art as well as music. Children can more easily remember and be touched by songs that have images associated with them.

We think of this songbook as primarily a parent/child book, for use in the home with or without piano or guitar accompaniment. Churches, however, can also benefit from this carefully selected core of songs in Christian education settings or with young children's choirs. The indexes are meant to assist teachers, choir directors and worship planners in their efforts to involve young children in the life of the church.

And finally, the book can be used by the young pianist. The simple keyboard accompaniments can be played by adults or children after several years of piano study. Guitar chords are also provided.

Music can be experienced in many ways, and the texts and melodies of many of these songs suggest the use of dance, movement, rhythm instruments, play acting, puppets, and painting or drawing. Exploring individual songs through several different media will reinforce the meaning of the text and imprint the tune in children's memories. And perhaps most importantly, children will experience music in a playful context.

This work was enriched by the enthusiasm and assistance of Patricia Roth Nuyken (Kodaly music specialist), Kim Patterson (children's choir director), Nancy Roth (clergywoman, specialist in children's hymnody and scholar in children and theology), Rebecca Slough (teacher of worship and hymnody), Wanda Stauffer (guitarist), Mary Louise VanDyke (Coordinator of the Dictionary of American Hymnology for the Hymn Society in the United States and Canada), David Breckbill (musicologist and writer), and Greg Slough (avid supporter). We thank them for their time, energy, and wisdom.

Linda S. Richer
Anita Stoltzfus Breckbill

# God's World
## and Nature

# All creatures of the earth and sky

1. All crea-tures of the earth and sky, with
2. Great rush-ing winds and bree-zes soft, you
3. Swift flow-ing wa-ter, pure and clear, make
4. Dear moth-er earth, you day by day un -

glad-ness lift your voic-es high. Al - le - lu - ia, al - le -
clouds that ride the winds a - loft, Al - le - lu - ia, al - le -
mu - sic for your God to hear. Al - le - lu - ia, al - le -
fold your bless-ings on our way. Al - le - lu - ia, al - le -

lu - ia! Bright burn - ing sun with gold - en
lu - ia! Fair ris - ing morn, in praise re -
lu - ia! Fire so in - tense and fierce - ly
lu - ia! All flow'rs and fruits that in you

beams,    pale    sil - ver moon that   gent - ly   gleams.
joice,    stars   night-ly   shin - ing   find    a     voice.
bright,   you    give to    us    both warmth and    light.
grow,    let    them in    glo - ry   al - so     show.

O

praise God,   al - le - lu - ia,   al - le - lu - ia!   Al - le -

lu - ia,   al - le - lu - ia!

Words: Francis of Assisi, 1182-1226; tr. William H. Draper, 1855-1933, alt., © J. Curwen and Sons
Music: LASST UNS ERFREUEN, *Geistliche Kirchengesänge,* Cologne, 1623

# Morning has broken

Morn-ing has bro - ken like the first morn - ing.

Black-bird has spo - ken like the first bird.

Praise for the sing - ing! Praise for the morn - ing!

Praise for them, spring - ing fresh from the Word!

Words: Eleanor Farjeon, 1881-1965, alt., © David Higham Assoc., Ltd.
Music: BUNESSAN, Gaelic traditional

# For the beauty of the earth

1. For the beauty of the earth, for the splen-dor of the skies, for the love which from our birth o - ver and a - round us lies,
2. For the won-der of each hour of the day and of the night, hill and vale, and tree and flow'r, sun and moon, and stars of light, God of all, to you we raise this our hymn of grate-ful praise.
3. For the joy of hu-man love, broth-er, sis-ter, par-ent, child, friends on earth, and friends a - bove, for all gen-tle thoughts and mild,

Words: Folliott S. Pierpoint, 1835-1917, alt.
Music: DIX, melody arr. from Conrad Kocher, 1786-1872, by William H. Monk, 1823-1889

# Praise to God

1. Praise to God, praise to God, for the green-ness
2. Thanks to God, thanks to God, for the gift of
3. Sing to God, sing to God, for the grace of

of the trees, for the beau - ty of the flow'rs,
friends in Christ, for the church, our house of faith,
Je - sus Christ, for the love of par - ent God,

for the blue - ness of the sky,
for the gift of won - drous love,
for the com - fort and the strength

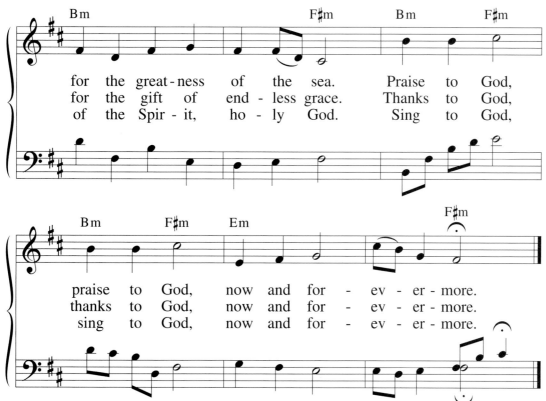

for the great-ness of the sea. Praise to God,
for the gift of end-less grace. Thanks to God,
of the Spir-it, ho-ly God. Sing to God,

praise to God, now and for - ev - er - more.
thanks to God, now and for - ev - er - more.
sing to God, now and for - ev - er - more.

Words: Nobuaki Hanaoka, © 1983, Japanese United Methodist Church
Music: SAKURA, Japanese traditional; music tr. © 1983, Abingdon Press, admin. by the COPYRIGHT CO., Nashville, TN. All Rights Reserved. International
Copyright Secured. Used By Permission. Harm. by Jonathan McNair, © 1993, Pilgrim Press

1. Come, O God of all the earth. Come to us, O
2. Come, O God of flash - ing light, twin - kling star and
3. Come, O God of snow and rain. Show - er down up -

right - eous one. Come, and bring our love to birth
burn - ing sun. God of day and God of night;
on the earth. Come, O God of joy and pain;

in the glo - ry of your son.
in your light we all are one. Sing out,
God of sor - row, God of mirth.

earth and skies! Sing of the God who loves you! Raise your

joy - ful cries! Dance to the life a - round you!

Words: Marty Haugen, b. 1950
Music: SING OUT, Marty Haugen, b. 1950
© 1985, GIA Publications, Inc.

1. The earth - worm in the soil, the
2. Help us to un - der - stand all
3. The gi - ant hump - back whale, the

flow - er and the bee, are part of God's im -
crea - tures have a part. We're not the on - ly
ti - ny ba - by dove, are part of God's im -

mense de - sign if we have eyes to
ones to be close to God's lov - ing
mense de - sign for

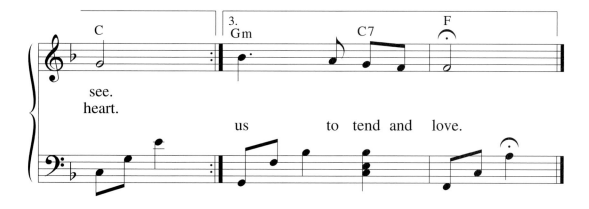

see.
heart.

us      to tend and love.

*Stanzas for older children:*

The yellow butterfly
who flutters tiny wings
may cause winds far away to blow.
There are no separate things.

May we not hurt God's earth
through selfishness and greed,
or use too much of what there is
when others are in need.

Words: Nancy Roth, b. 1936, © 1997
Music: ORR, Robert Roth, b. 1928

Words: Mexican traditional, comp. by ed. from tr. in the *New Century Hymnal,* 1995, and Alice Firgau, 1988,
© Chandos Music, Inc.
Music: DE COLORES, Mexican traditional

In the bulb there is a flow - er; in the seed, an ap - ple

tree; in co - coons, a hid - den prom - ise: but - ter -

flies will soon be free! In the cold and snow of

win - ter there's a spring that waits to be un - re -

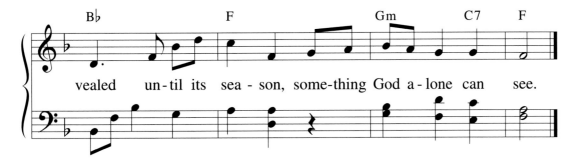

vealed un-til its sea - son, some-thing God a-lone can see.

Words: Natalie Sleeth, 1930-1992
Music: HYMN OF PROMISE, Natalie Sleeth, 1930-1992

1. Each lit-tle flow'r that o - pens, each lit-tle bird that
2. The pur-ple head-ed moun-tain, the riv-er run-ning
3. The cold winds in the win - ter, the pleas-ant sum-mer

sings, God made their glow-ing col - ors and made their grace-ful
by, the sun-set and the morn-ing that bright-ens up the
sun, the ripe fruits in the gar - den, God made them ev - 'ry

wings.
sky. Yes, all things bright and beau - ti-ful, all crea-tures great and
one.

small, and all things wise and won-der-ful, our great God made them all.

Words: Cecil Frances Alexander, 1823-1895, alt.
Music: DANISH TUNE, Danish traditional

# Many and great

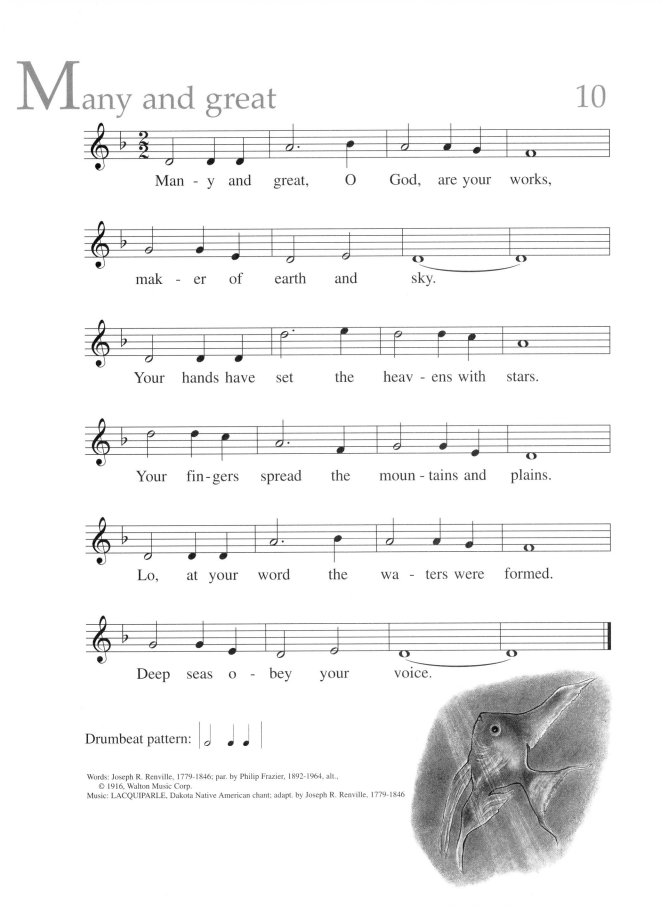

Man - y and great, O God, are your works,

mak - er of earth and sky.

Your hands have set the heav - ens with stars.

Your fin - gers spread the moun - tains and plains.

Lo, at your word the wa - ters were formed.

Deep seas o - bey your voice.

Drumbeat pattern:

Words: Joseph R. Renville, 1779-1846; par. by Philip Frazier, 1892-1964, alt.,
© 1916, Walton Music Corp.
Music: LACQUIPARLE, Dakota Native American chant; adapt. by Joseph R. Renville, 1779-1846

Words: Brian Howard, 20th cent., alt.
Music: THE BUTTERFLY SONG, Brian Howard
© 1974, Mission Hills Music, admin. by THE COPYRIGHT CO.,
    Nashville, TN. All Rights Reserved. International Copyright Secured.
    Used By Permission.

# Joyful, joyful, we adore you

1. Joy - ful, joy - ful, we a - dore you, God of glo - ry,
2. All your works with joy sur - round you. Earth and heav'n re -

God of love. Hearts un - fold like flow'rs be - fore you,
flect your rays. Stars and plan - ets sing a - round you,

o - p'ning to the sun a - bove. Melt the clouds of
cen - ter of un - bro - ken praise. Field and for - est,

sin and sad - ness. Drive the dark of doubt a - way.
vale and moun - tain, bloom - ing mead - ow, flash - ing sea,

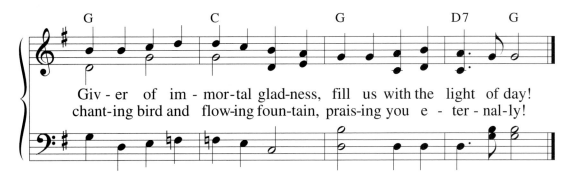

Giv - er of im - mor-tal glad-ness, fill us with the light of day!
chant-ing bird and flow-ing foun-tain, prais-ing you e - ter - nal-ly!

Words: Henry van Dyke, 1852-1933, alt.
Music: HYMN TO JOY, Ludwig van Beethoven, 1770-1827; adapt. by Edward Hodges, 1796-1867; harm. by Jack Burnam, © 1994, alt. All rights reserved.

# Praise
## to God

# Praise and thanksgiving

**Round**

1. Praise and thanks-giv-ing let ev-'ry-one bring
2. All peo-ple, join us and sing out God's praise.
3. May we go out from here God's love to share.

un-to our God___ for ev-'ry good thing.
For ev-'ry bless-ing your hap-py songs raise.
Sing-ing out God's love to all ev-'ry - where.

All to-geth - er joy-ful - ly sing!

Words: St. 1, Alsatian traditional; tr. Edith Lovell Thomas, 1950, alt.; st. 2-3, Marie Post, © 1987, CRC Publications, alt.
Music: LOBET UND PREISET, Alsatian traditional; harm. from *Sing for joy,* © 1961, Seabury press

# Full of kindness and compassion 14

1. Full of kind - ness and com - pas - sion,
2. See the trees spread out their branch - es.
3. All the earth says thank you, thank you.

slow to an - ger, vast in love, God is good to
All the flow - ers o - pen wide. Sun - shine spar - kles
Birds are sing - ing, o - ceans roar. For your good - ness

all cre - a - tion, all the earth God's good - ness proves.
on the wa - ter, for all crea - tures God pro - vides.
pours up - on us. And your love is ev - er sure.

Words: St. 1, Richard Mant, 1776-1848, alt., based on Psalm 145:8-10; st. 2-3, Jean Janzen, b. 1933, © 1997
Music: STUTTGART, Christian Friedrich Witt, 1660-1716, *Psalmodia sacra,* 1715

# O sing to the Lord

# Amen, we praise your name, O God  16

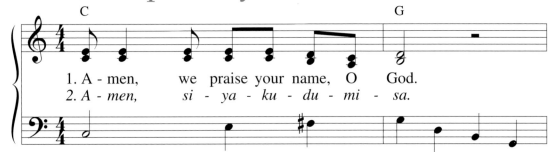

1. A - men,    we praise your name, O God.
2. *A - men,    si - ya - ku - du - mi - sa.*

A-men, we praise your name, O God.    A-men, a-men,
*A-men, si - ya - ku - du - mi - sa.    A-men, Ba-ba,*

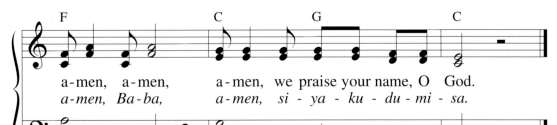

a-men, a-men,    a-men, we praise your name, O God.
*a-men, Ba-ba,    a-men, si - ya - ku - du - mi - sa.*

Words: South African traditional
Music: ASITHI: AMEN, attr. to Stephan Cuthbert Molefe, c1915-1987,
    as taught by George Mxadana

# Now thank we all our God

Now thank we all our God, with hearts, and hands and voic-es, who won-drous things has done, in whom the world re-joic-es; who from our moth-er's arms has blessed us on our way with count-less gifts of love, and still is ours to-day.

Words: *Nun danket alle Gott,* Martin Rinkart, 1586-1649; tr. Catherine Winkworth, 1827-1878, alt.
Music: NUN DANKET, Johann Crüger, 1598-1662; harm. by Margaret W. Mealy, b. 1922, © 1981, GIA Publications

# Alleluia, alleluia

Words and music: Palestinian traditional

# Laudate Dominum

1. *Lau - da - te          Do - mi - num,          lau - da - te*
2. Praise God    in       ev - 'ry land.          Praise God    all
3. *Praise God    for      _ _ _.                  Praise God    for

*Do - mi - num          om - nes          gen - tes,*
peo - ple.              Sing    out       prais - es.
_ _ _.                  Sing    out       prais - es.

Al - le - lu - ia.          Al - le - lu - ia.

*\*Children can fill in blanks.*

Words: Based on Psalm 117, Taizé Community, 1980; tr. by ed.
Music: LAUDATE DOMINUM, melody and harm. by Jacques Berthier, 1923-1994
© 1980, Les Presses de Taizé, GIA Publications, Inc., agent

# Sing, sing, praise and sing

**Refrain**

Sing, sing, praise and sing! Hon-or God for ev-'ry-thing.

Sing to God and let it ring. Sing and praise and sing! **Fine**

**Verses**

1. Clap your hands, lift your voice, praise our God and re-joice!
2. Full of joy, full of rest, through our God, we are blessed.
3. Cym-bal, harp, vi-o-lin, tam-bou-rine, all join in! **D.C.**

Words: Elizabeth Syré, South Africa, alt.
Music: SING, SING, PRAISE AND SING, South African traditional; adapt. by Elizabeth Syré

# Praise God from whom all blessings flow 21

Words: V. Maasilaamaani; adapt. by D.T. Niles, alt.
Music: THUDHI, V. Maasilaamaani
© 1990, Asian Institute for Liturgy and Music (AILM), and Christian Conference of Asia (CCA)

# Praise God from whom all blessings flow 22

Praise God, from whom all bless - ings flow. Praise
God, all crea - tures here be - low. Cre -
a - tor, Sav - ior, Spir - it, praise, in
joy - ful song through all our days.

*Alternate text:*

Praise God, from whom all blessings flow.
Praise him, all creatures here below.
Praise him above, ye heavenly host.
Praise Father, Son, and Holy Ghost.

Words: Thomas Ken, 1637-1711; alt. by Michael Kuhn
Music: OLD 100th, Louis Bourgeois, c1510-c1561

# Prayers
## to God

# Good morning

1. Good morn-ing, God, the night is gone.
2. God, grant that in the morn-ing light

We bring to you a morn-ing song.
we see things clear - ly and a - right.

Now chase the shades of night a - way
God, as we greet this fresh new day

and turn the dark - ness in - to day.
take an - ger, fear, and doubt a - way.

Words: Ken Medema, alt., © 1988, Brier Patch Music
Music: O WALY WALY, English traditional

# Ev'ry morning brings us blessings  24

F       C      Dm  A  Dm     C      F

1. Ev - 'ry morn - ing   brings us   bless-ings from a - bove,
2. Sun - shine for our   gar - dens,  rain for flow-er  beds,
3. Since our God in   heav - en  gives us  ev - 'ry - thing,

C7      F   C   F   C7     F

food up - on our   ta - bles,  arms to care and   love.
in the night God's stars  shine  on my sleep-ing   head.
lov - ing - ly and glad - ly  now our gifts we   bring.

Words: St. 1-2, Jean Janzen, b. 1933, © 1997; st. 3, anonymous
Music: CASWALL, Friedrich Filitz, 1804-1876

# For your gracious blessing

**Round**

For your gra-cious bless-ing, for your won-drous word,

for your lov-ing kind-ness, we give thanks, O God.

Words and music: Traditional

# A bird, a lovely butterfly

1. A bird, a love-ly but-ter-fly, a
2. A dai-sy, rose or daf-fo-dil, the
3. For gen-tle rain, the qui-et snow, for

fleec-y cloud up in the sky, a might-y moun-tain,
green grass grow-ing on the hill, the wood-lands, friend-ly,
sun, and moon, and star-light glow, for all the beau-ty

wide and high, all speak of you, O God.
deep and still, all speak of you, O God.
that we know our thanks to you, O God.

Words: Florence Pedigo Jansson, © 1965, The Hymn Society. Admin. by Hope Publishing Co., Carol Stream, IL 60188. All rights reserved. Used by permission.
Music: CHILDHOOD, Henry Walford Davies, 1869-1941, from *A Students' Hymnal*, 1923

# For health and strength

**Round**

1. For health and strength and
2. For neigh - bors, friends, and
3. For faith and hope and

dai - ly food,
fam - i - ly, we give you thanks, O God.
lov - ing care,

# To God who gives us daily bread — 28

To God who gives us dai - ly bread a
thank - ful song we raise and pray that God who
sends us food will fill our hearts with praise.

Words: Attr. to Mary Rumsey, alt.
Music: TALLIS ORDINAL, Thomas Tallis, c1505-1585

# I pray when I talk with God

1. I pray when I talk with God. I pray when I talk with God. Shar - ing sad - ness, joys and needs, I pray when I talk with God.
2. I pray when I think of God. I pray when I think of God. Won - d'ring and i - mag - in - ing, I pray when I think of God.
3. I pray when I work with God. I pray when I work with God. Help - ing make a bet - ter world, I pray when I work with God.
4. I pray when I rest with God. I pray when I rest with God. Full of won - der and of love, I pray when I rest with God.

Words: Nancy Roth, b. 1936, © 1997
Music: PRAYER, Robert Roth, b. 1928

# All praise to you, my God, this night 30

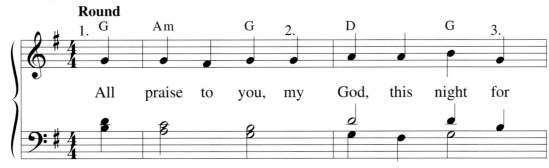

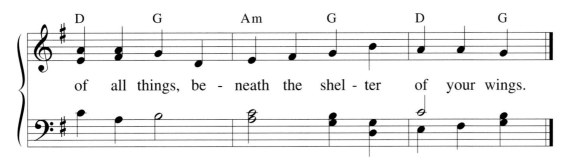

Words: Thomas Ken, 1637-1711, alt.
Music: TALLIS CANON, Thomas Tallis, c1505-1585

# All night, all day

31

**Refrain**

All night, all day, an-gels watch-ing o-ver me, my Lord.

All night, all day, an-gels watch-ing o-ver me.  **Fine**

**Verses**

1. Now I lay me down to sleep.
2. Lord, stay with me through the night.

An-gels watch-ing o-ver me, my Lord.  Pray the Lord my
An-gels watch-ing o-ver me, my Lord.  Wake me with the

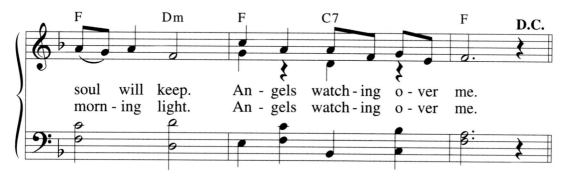

soul will keep. An - gels watch - ing o - ver me.
morn - ing light. An - gels watch - ing o - ver me.

Words and music: ALL NIGHT, ALL DAY, African-American traditional

# God's
# Stories

1. God cre - at - ed heav'n and earth, all things
2. Let us praise God's mer - cy great! All our

per - fect brought to birth. God's great pow'r made dark and
needs that love a - wait; God who fash - ions all that

light, earth re - volv - ing day and night.
lives, to each one a bless - ing gives.

Words: Taiwanese traditional hymn; tr. Boris and Clare Anderson, © 1983
Music: THE CALL, Ralph Vaughan Williams, 1872-1958

# Ol' Noah got mad

*Solo* G
1. Ol' No-ah got mad, 'cause the rain kept a-drop-pin'.
2. He built him an ark 'cause the rain kept a-drop-pin'.
3. He float-ed the ark while the rain kept a-drop-pin'.
4. And when the rain stopped No-ah stopped all the mop-pin'.

*All* Em    G    D7    G
Did-n't it rain? O did-n't it rain?

*Solo* G
It rained for-ty days, for-ty nights with-out stop-pin'.
The an-i-mals came two by two with-out stop-pin'.
Un-til No-ah saw that the rain was a-stop-pin'.
The rain-bow ap-peared when the rain stopped a-drop-pin'.

*All* Em    G    D7    G
Did-n't it rain? O did-n't it rain?

Words: Traditional; adapt. by Barbara B. Bartlett, © 1994, Selah Publishing Co., Inc.
Music: NOAH'S ARK, traditional

# Who built the ark?

**Refrain** G        D7        G

*Solo*      *All*      *Solo*      *All*

Who built the ark? No-ah! No-ah! Who built the ark? Broth-er

D7     G **Fine**     **Verses**   G

No-ah built the ark.    1. Old man No-ah   built the ark.    He

Em     G     D7     G

built it out of the hick-o-ry bark.    He built it long, both

Em     G     D7     G **D.C.**

wide and tall,    with plen-ty of room for the   large and small.

*Verses 2-6:*

2. In came the animals, two by two,
   hippopotamus and kangaroo.
   In came the animals, three by three.
   two big cats and a bumble bee.

3. In came the animals, four by four,
   two through the window and two through the door.
   In came the animals, five by five,
   the bees came swarming from the hive.

4. In came the animals, six by six,
   elephant laughed at the monkey's tricks.
   In came the animals, seven by seven,
   giraffes and the camels looking up to heaven.

5. In came the animals, eight by eight,
   some on time and the others were late.
   In came the animals, nine by nine,
   some were laughin' and some were cryin'.

6. In came the animals, ten by ten,
   time for the voyage to begin.
   Noah said, "Go shut the door.
   The rain's started fallin' and we can't take more."

Words and music: African-American traditional

1. We are climb-ing Ja-cob's lad-der.
2. Ev-'ry round goes high-er, high-er.

We are climb-ing Ja-cob's lad-der. We are climb-ing
Ev-'ry round goes high-er, high-er. Ev-'ry round goes

Ja-cob's lad-der; chil-dren of the Lord.
high-er, high-er; chil-dren of the Lord.

Words and music: JACOB'S LADDER, African-American traditional

Words and music: GO DOWN MOSES, African-American traditional

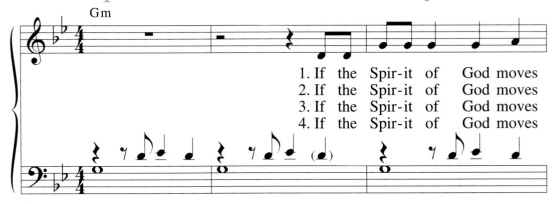

Gm

1. If the Spir-it of God moves
2. If the Spir-it of God moves
3. If the Spir-it of God moves
4. If the Spir-it of God moves

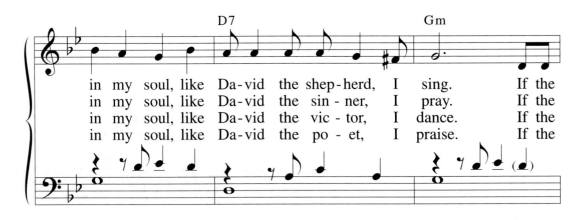

D7      Gm

in my soul, like Da-vid the shep-herd, I sing. If the
in my soul, like Da-vid the sin - ner, I pray. If the
in my soul, like Da-vid the vic - tor, I dance. If the
in my soul, like Da-vid the po - et, I praise. If the

D7

Spir-it of God moves in my soul, like Da-vid the shep-herd, I
Spir-it of God moves in my soul, like Da-vid the sin - ner, I
Spir-it of God moves in my soul, like Da-vid the vic - tor, I
Spir-it of God moves in my soul, like Da-vid the po - et, I

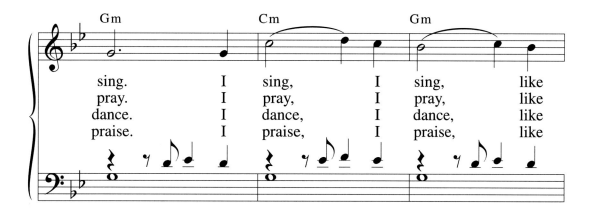

sing.      I   sing,      I   sing,    like
pray.      I   pray,      I   pray,    like
dance.      I   dance,      I   dance,    like
praise.      I   praise,      I   praise,    like

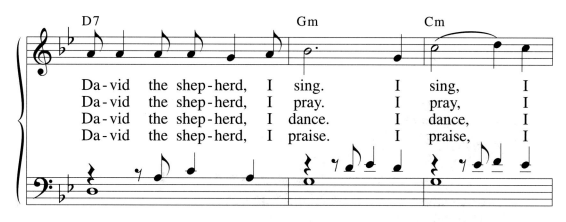

Da-vid   the shep-herd,  I  sing.     I   sing,      I
Da-vid   the shep-herd,  I  pray.     I   pray,      I
Da-vid   the shep-herd,  I  dance.     I   dance,      I
Da-vid   the shep-herd,  I  praise.     I   praise,      I

sing,     like   Da-vid   the shep-herd,  I  sing.
pray,     like   Da-vid   the shep-herd,  I  pray.
dance,     like   Da-vid   the shep-herd,  I  dance.
praise,     like   Da-vid   the shep-herd,  I  praise.

Words: Anonymous Spanish; tr. Mennonite World Conference, alt., © 1978
Music: LIKE DAVID THE SHEPHERD, I SING, traditional

1. Glo - ry, glo - ry hal - le - lu - jah, since I
2. I am danc - ing Mir - iam's dance now, since I
3. Feel like shout - ing "Hal - le - lu - jah!" since I

laid my bur-dens down. Glo - ry, glo - ry hal - le -
laid my bur-dens down. I am danc - ing Mir-iam's
laid my bur-dens down. Feel like shout-ing "Hal - le -

lu - jah, since I laid my bur-dens down.
dance now, since I laid my bur-dens down.
lu - jah!" since I laid my bur-dens down.

Words and music: African-American traditional

Words: Based on Psalm 23, *The Psalms of David in Meeter,* 1650
Music: CRIMOND, Jessie Seymour Irvine, 1836-1887

# God Cares
## for Me

# Little children, never fear

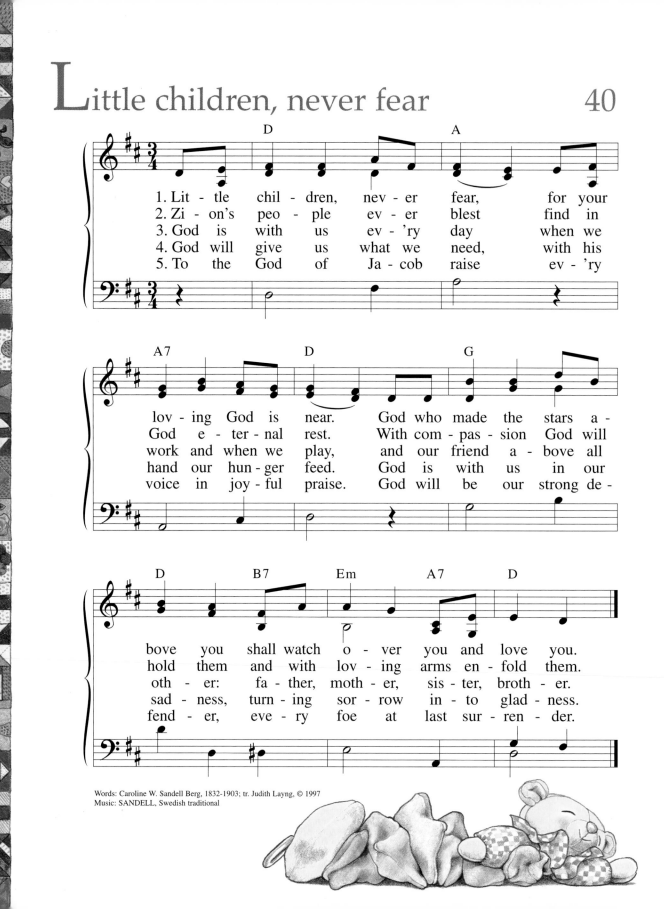

1. Lit - tle chil - dren, nev - er fear, for your lov - ing God is near. God who made the stars a - bove you shall watch o - ver you and love you.
2. Zi - on's peo - ple ev - er blest find in God e - ter - nal rest. With com - pas - sion God will hold them and with lov - ing arms en - fold them.
3. God is with us ev - 'ry day when we work and when we play, and our friend a - bove all oth - er: fa - ther, moth - er, sis - ter, broth - er.
4. God will give us what we need, with his hand our hun - ger feed. God is with us in our sad - ness, turn - ing sor - row in - to glad - ness.
5. To the God of Ja - cob raise ev - 'ry voice in joy - ful praise. God will be our strong de - fend - er, eve - ry foe at last sur - ren - der.

Words: Caroline W. Sandell Berg, 1832-1903; tr. Judith Layng, © 1997
Music: SANDELL, Swedish traditional

# Amazing grace

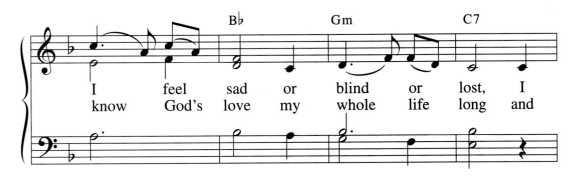

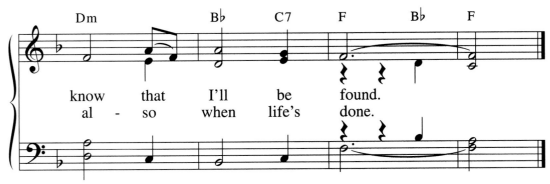

Words: Nancy Roth, b. 1936, after John Newton, 1725-1807, © 1997
Music: NEW BRITAIN, from *Virginia Harmony*, 1831

# God has sent the angels down

1. God has sent the an - gels down.
2. God has sent the an - gels down.

They are with me, all a - round. Safe they keep me
They are with me, all a - round. They pro - tect me

all the day, while I work and when I play.
through the night. Glad I wake with morn - ing light.

Words: Martha Jander, b. 1943, alt., © 1989, Concordia Publishing House
Music: ORIENTIS PATRIBUS, Pierre de Corbeil, d. 1222; harm. from *Little ones sing praise*,
    © 1989, Concordia Publishing House

# When our hearts are full of pain

1. When our hearts are full of pain,
2. When our dear-est ones have gone,
3. When the world de - lights our eyes,

God is there; and when our tears fall
God is there; and when we feel we're
God is there; and when a day brings

like the rain, God is there.
left a - lone, God is there. For
us sur - prise, God is there.

God is like our cloth - ing, wrap-ping us with love.

Words: Nancy Roth, b. 1936, after Julian of Norwich, 14th cent., © 1997
Music: CONSOLATION, attr. to Elkanah Kelsay Dare, 1782-1826

# For God so loved us

**D / G / D / G**

1. For God so loved us, God sent the sav - ior, for God so
2. *Gott ist die Lie - be, lässt mich er - lö - sen. Gott ist die*

**Em7 / A / D / A7**

loved us, and loves me too. Love so un - end - ing, I'll sing your
*Lie - be. Er liebt auch mich. Drum sag ich noch ein-mal. Gott ist die*

**D / Em7 / A / D**

prais - es. God loves all chil - dren, loves e - ven me.
*Lie - be. Gott ist die Lie - be. Er liebt auch mich.*

Words: August Rische, d. 1906; tr. Esther C. Bergen, alt., © 1956, Faith and Life Press
Music: GOTT IST DIE LIEBE, German traditional

# Go to sleep and peace be with you  45

Go to sleep and peace be with you, all through the night.

Guard-ian an-gels, God will send you, all through the night.

Slow the qui-et hours are creep-ing. Ev-'ry-thing is soft-ly sleep-ing.

God a lov-ing watch is keep-ing all through the night.

Words: Harold Boulton, 19th cent., alt.
Music: AR HYD Y NOS, Welsh traditional

# Birth
of Jesus

# Joy to the world

1. Joy to the world, the Lord is come! Let
2. Joy to the earth, the Sav - ior reigns! Let

earth re - ceive her king. Let ev - 'ry
all our songs em - ploy, while fields and

heart pre - pare him room, and heav'n and na - ture
floods, rocks, hills and plains, re - peat the sound - ing

sing, and heav'n and na - ture sing, and
joy, re - peat the sound - ing joy, re -

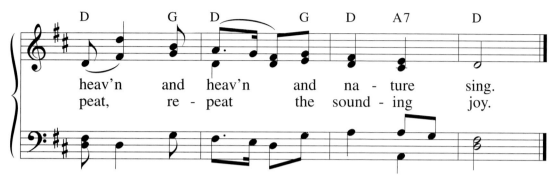

| D | G | D | G | D | A7 | D |

heav'n      and      heav'n      and      na - ture      sing.
peat,      re - peat      the      sound - ing      joy.

Text: Based on Psalm 98; Isaac Watts, 1674-1748
Music: ANTIOCH; arr. from George F. Handel, 1685-1759, in Thomas Hawkes' *Collection of tunes,* 1833; harm. by Owen Burdick, b. 1954, © 1994

# Mary had a baby

47

Words: St. 1, African-American traditional; st. 2-4, Ruth Crawford Seeger, 1901-1953
Music: African-American traditional; harm. from *Little ones sing praise*, © 1989, Concordia Publishing House

# Jesus came on Christmas day

1. Je - sus came on Christ-mas day. Wreathe the hol - ly,
2. Love to him on Christ-mas morn. Love to ev - 'ry

twine the bay. *Je - sus na - tus ho - di - e, the
ba - by born. Je - sus na - tus ho - di - e, the

lit - tle one, the babe, the son of Mar - y.
lit - tle one, the babe, the son of Mar - y.

*Translation: Jesus was born today.

Words: German traditional; par. by Vincent Brown Silliman, b. 1894
Music: RESONET IN LAUDIBUS; German traditional, 14th cent.

# Jesus our brother, kind and good    49

*Verses 4-6:*

4. "I," said the sheep with curly horn,
   "I gave him my wool for his blanket warm.
   He wore my coat on Christmas morn.
   I," said the sheep with curly horn.

5. "I," said the dove from rafters high,
   "I cooed him to sleep, so he should not cry.
   We cooed him to sleep, my mate and I.
   I," said the dove from rafters high.

6. Thus every beast by some good spell,
   in the stable dark was glad to tell
   of the gift he gave Emmanuel,
   the gift he gave Emmanuel.

Words: Traditional English carol
Music: ORIENTIS PARTIBUS, Pierre de Corbeil, d. 1222;
   harm. by Margaret Mealy, b. 1922, from *Sing for Joy.*
   © 1961, Seabury Press

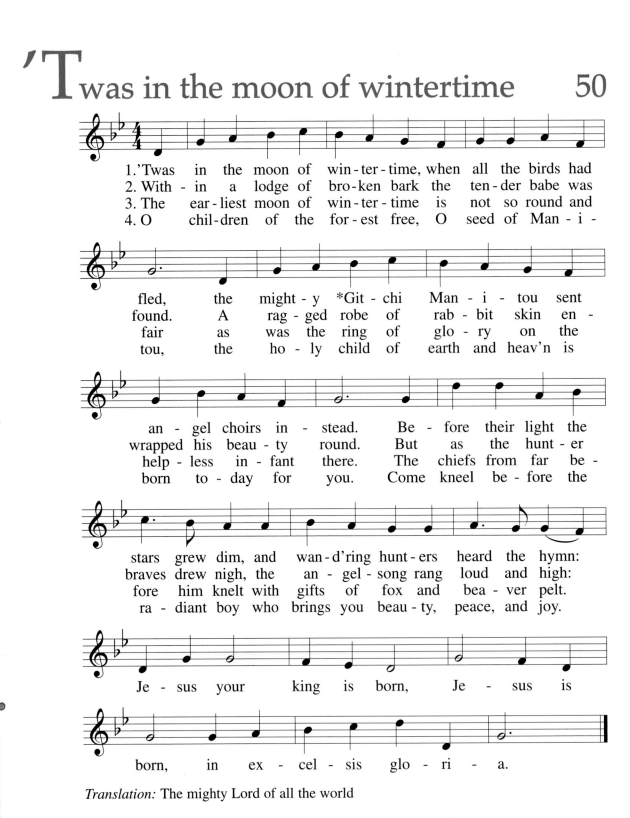

1. 'Twas in the moon of win-ter-time, when all the birds had
2. With-in a lodge of bro-ken bark the ten-der babe was
3. The ear-liest moon of win-ter-time is not so round and
4. O chil-dren of the for-est free, O seed of Man-i-

fled, the might-y *Git-chi Man-i-tou sent
found. A rag-ged robe of rab-bit skin en-
fair as was the ring of glo-ry on the
tou, the ho-ly child of earth and heav'n is

an-gel choirs in-stead. Be-fore their light the
wrapped his beau-ty round. But as the hunt-er
help-less in-fant there. The chiefs from far be-
born to-day for you. Come kneel be-fore the

stars grew dim, and wan-d'ring hunt-ers heard the hymn:
braves drew nigh, the an-gel-song rang loud and high:
fore him knelt with gifts of fox and bea-ver pelt.
ra-diant boy who brings you beau-ty, peace, and joy.

Je-sus your king is born, Je-sus is

born, in ex-cel-sis glo-ri-a.

*Translation:* The mighty Lord of all the world

Words: St. Jean de Brebeuf, d. 1649, *Estennial de tsonue Jesus ahatonhia,* ca. 1643; tr. Jesse E. Middleton, 1872-1960, © Fredrick Harris Music Co. Ltd.
Music: UNE JEUNE PUCELLE, French traditional, 16th cent.

# O come, little children

51

1. O come, lit-tle chil-dren, O come, one and all. O come to the cra-dle in Beth-le-hem's stall. Come look in the man-ger, there sleeps on the hay, an in-fant so love-ly, in light bright as day.

2. The hay is his pil-low, the man-ger his bed. The beasts stand in won-der to gaze on his head. Yet there, in the sta-ble, so hum-ble and poor, come shep-herds and wise-men to kneel at his door.

3. O bow with the shep-herds on low bend-ed knee, with hearts full of thanks for the gift which you see. Come, lift up your voic-es the child to a-dore. Sing joy to the world, love and peace ev-er-more.

Words: Christian von Schmidt, 1768-1854; tr. unknown
Music: IHR KINDERLEIN KOMMET, Johann Abraham Peter Schulz, 1747-1800

# Away in a manger

1. A - way in a man - ger, no crib for his bed, the
2. The cat - tle are low - ing, the ba - by a - wakes, but
3. Be near me, Lord Je - sus. I ask you to stay close

lit - tle Lord Je - sus laid down his sweet head. The
lit - tle Lord Je - sus no cry - ing he makes. I
by me for - ev - er, and love me I pray. Bless

stars in the bright sky looked down where he lay, the
love you Lord Je - sus! Look down from the sky, and
all the dear chil - dren in your ten - der care, and

lit - tle Lord Je - sus a - sleep on the hay.
stay by my side un - til morn - ing is nigh.
fit us for heav - en to live with you there.

Words: St. 1-2, anonymous; st. 3, John T. McFarland, 1851-1913
Music: CRADLE SONG, William James Kirkpatrick, 1838-1921

# Away in a manger

1. A-way in a man-ger, no crib for his bed, the lit-tle Lord Je-sus laid down his sweet head. The stars in the sky looked down where he lay, the lit-tle Lord Je-sus, a-sleep on the hay.

2. The cat-tle are low-ing, the ba-by a-wakes, but lit-tle Lord Je-sus no cry-ing he makes. I love you Lord Je-sus! Look down from the sky, and stay by my side un-til morn-ing is nigh.

3. Be near me, Lord Je-sus. I ask you to stay close by me for-ev-er, and love me I pray. Bless all the dear chil-dren in your ten-der care, and fit us for heav-en to live with you there.

Words: St. 1-2, anonymous; st. 3, John T. McFarland, 1851-1913
Music: MUELLER, James Ramsey Murray, 1841-1905; harm. from *The Children's hymnary,* 1968, alt.

# Lully, lullay, O little tiny child

Lul - ly, lul - lay, O lit - tle ti - ny child, bye, bye, lul - ly, lul - lay. Lul - ly, lul - lay, O lit - tle ti - ny child, bye, bye, lul - ly, lul - lay.

Words and music: COVENTRY CAROL, English traditional, 16th cent.

# Shepherds came to Bethlehem

1. Shep - herds came to Beth - le - hem on Christ - mas day.
2. Then a shep - herd beat up - on a lit - tle drum.
3. As the shep - herds bowed be - fore the bless - ed boy,

How the ba - by smiled as pipes and flutes did play.
How it pleased the ba - by with its rum - tum - tum.
all the heav - ens rang with sounds of won - drous joy.

Glo - ry, sing glo - ry to God in the high - est, and

peace on earth, peace on earth.

Words: Rosemary Jacques, alt.
Music: PRZYBIEZELI, Polish traditional; harm. by Francis Girard, alt.
© 1974, General Learning Corporation

1. On this day earth shall ring
2. God's bright star, o'er his head,
3. On this day an - gels sing;

with the song chil-dren sing to the Lord, Christ our king,
wise men three to him led. Kneel they low by his bed,
with their song earth shall ring, prais - ing Christ, heav-en's king,

born on earth to save us; Je - sus who God gave us.
lay their gifts be - fore him, praise him and a - dore him.
born on earth to save us; peace and love he gave us.

*Id - e - o - o - o, Id - e - o - o - o,

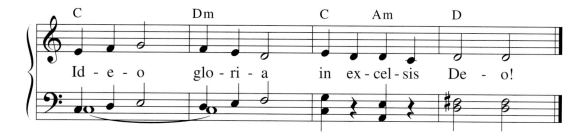

Id - e - o glo - ri - a in ex - cel - sis De - o!

*Translation:* Therefore, glory to God in the highest.

Words: *Piae cantiones,* 1582; tr. Jane M. Joseph, 1894-1929, © J. Curwen and Sons, Ltd., London
Music: PERSONENT HODIE, *Piae cantiones,* 1582

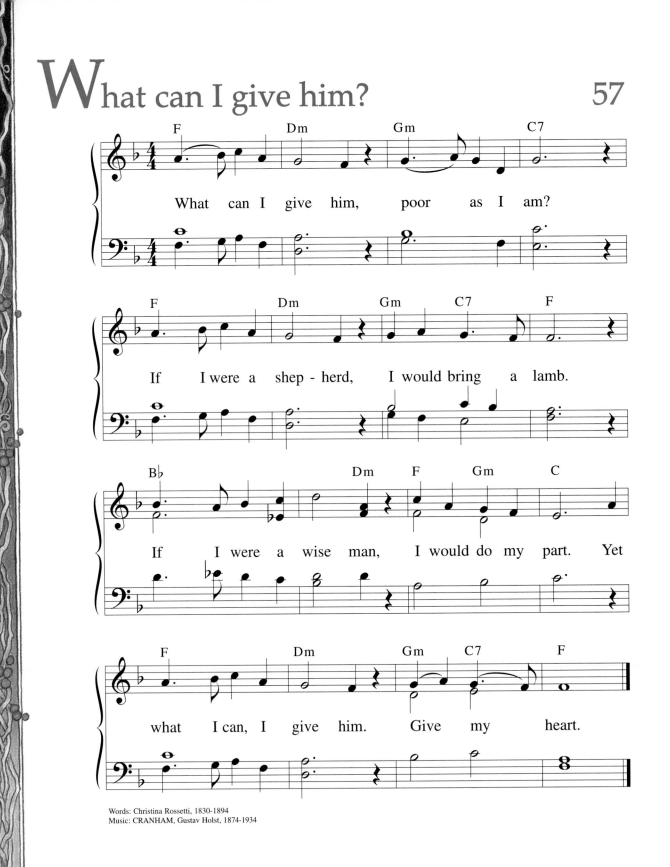

Words: Christina Rossetti, 1830-1894
Music: CRANHAM, Gustav Holst, 1874-1934

# Oh, how joyfully

1. Oh, how joy - ful - ly, Oh, how hope - ful - ly,
2. Oh, how joy - ful - ly, Oh, how peace - ful - ly,
3. Oh, how joy - ful - ly, Oh, how thank - ful - ly,

waits the world on Christ - mas eve!
sleeps the world on Christ - mas night!
wakes the world on Christ - mas morn!

Love comes heal - ing, God re - veal - ing.
Sins are cov - ered, grace dis - cov - ered.
God has spo - ken, death is bro - ken.

Friends, be joy - ful and be - lieve!
In our dark - ness shines the light!
Al - le - lu - ia! Christ is born!

Words: St. 1, Johann D. Falk, 1768-1826; st. 2-3, Heinrich Holzschuher; tr. Harris Loewen, b. 1953; re-envisioned by Brian Wren, 1990,
© 1993, Hope Publishing Co., Carol Stream, IL 60188. All rights reserved. Used by permission.
Music: SICILIAN MARINERS, *The European magazine and London review*, 1792

# Jesus our Friend and Teacher

# Jesu, Jesu

**Refrain**

Je - su, Je - su, fill us with your love, show us how to serve the neigh-bors we have from you.

**Verses**

1. Neigh-bors are rich___ and poor. Neigh-bors are black___ and white. Neigh-bors are near - by and far a - way.
2. These are the ones we should serve. These are the ones we should love. All these are neigh-bors to us and you.

# When Jesus saw the fishermen 60

**Round**

G F G Dm

1. When Je - sus saw the fish - er - men in
2. They fol - lowed where he healed the sick and
3. And now his friends are ev - 'ry - where; the

G F G Dm G F

boats up - on the sea, he called to them, "Come,
gave the hun - gry bread. And oth - ers joined them
cir - cle once so small ex - tends a - round the

G Dm G F G

leave your nets and fol - low, fol - low me."
as they went, wher - ev - er Je - sus led.
whole wide world, for Je - sus calls us all.

Words: Edith Agnew, © 1953, Westminster/John Knox Press
Music: ST. STEPHEN, composed and harm. by Richard L. Van Oss, b. 1953, © 1994, CRC Publications

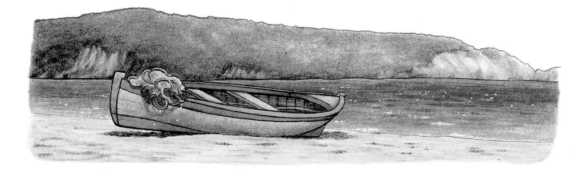

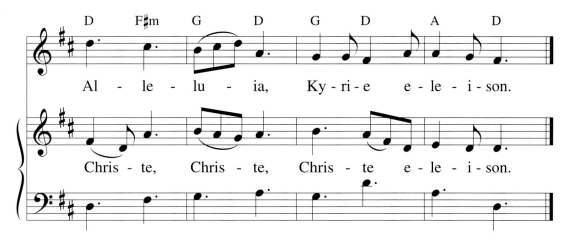

Al – le – lu – ia, Ky – ri – e    e – le – i – son.

Chris – te,    Chris – te,    Chris – te    e – le – i – son.

Words and music: COME AND SEE, Marilyn Houser Hamm, b. 1951, © 1974

# When Jesus the healer
62

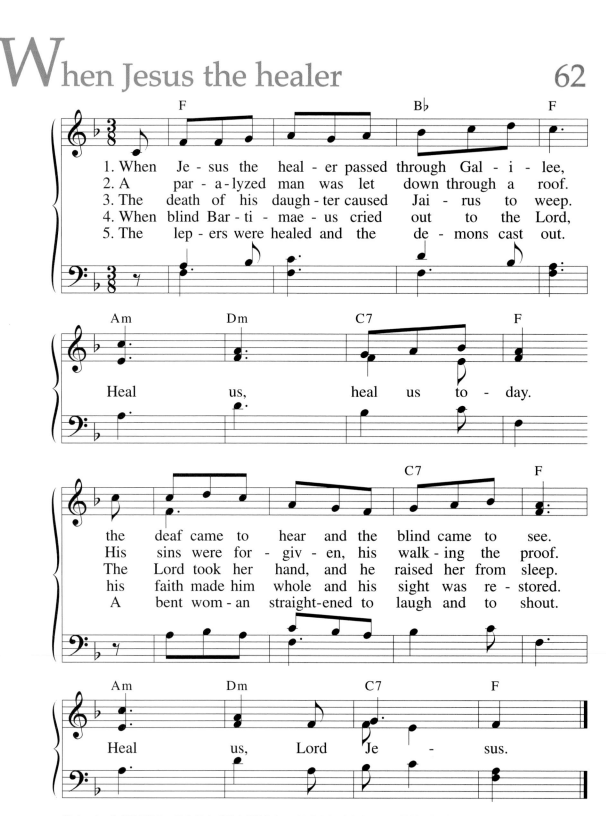

1. When Jesus the healer passed through Galilee,
2. A paralyzed man was let down through a roof.
3. The death of his daughter caused Jairus to weep.
4. When blind Bartimaeus cried out to the Lord,
5. The lepers were healed and the demons cast out.

Heal us, heal us today.

the deaf came to hear and the blind came to see.
His sins were forgiven, his walking the proof.
The Lord took her hand, and he raised her from sleep.
his faith made him whole and his sight was restored.
A bent woman straightened to laugh and to shout.

Heal us, Lord Jesus.

Words and music: HEALER, Peter D. Smith, b. 1938, © 1978, Stainer and Bell, Ltd. Admin. by Hope Publishing Co., Carol Stream, IL 60188. All rights reserved. Used by permsission.

# Guide my feet

Solo (G)      All   G    C    G

1. Guide    my    feet      while I run this race.
2. I'm      your   child     while I run this race.
3. Hold    my    hand     while I run this race.
4. Stand    by    me      while I run this race.

Solo (G)      All   G    C    G

Guide    my    feet      while I run this race.
I'm      your child     while I run this race.
Hold    my    hand     while I run this race.
Stand    by    me      while I run this race.

Solo (G)      All G    C    G

Guide    my    feet      while I run this race,      for I
I'm      your   child     while I run this race,
Hold    my    hand     while I run this race,
Stand    by    me      while I run this race,

C      G

don't want    to   run this race in   vain!

Words and music: African-American traditional

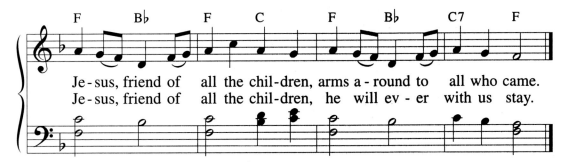

Je-sus, friend of all the chil-dren, arms a-round to all who came.
Je-sus, friend of all the chil-dren, he will ev-er with us stay.

Words: Walter John Mathams, 1853-1931; adapt. by Jean Janzen, b. 1933, © 1997
Music: PLEADING SAVIOR, American traditional

# Alleluia! Sing for joy

**Round**

1. Al - le - lu - ia! Sing for joy and
2. Je - sus, sav - ior, in a lone - ly
3. Je - sus, teach - er, show - ing us to

cel - e - brate. He rose in
world you love us. God give
love all peo - ple, love our

glo - ry. Je - sus is Lord.
cour - age. Christ give us strength.
neigh - bors. Christ gives us peace.

Words: Alf Siemens and Tom Graff, alt., © Grapple Press
Music: JESUS, JESUS, Thomas Ravenscroft, c1582-c1635

# Amigos de Cristo

A - mi - gos de Cris - to, we're friends of the Lord. A -
mi - gos de Cris - to, we're friends of the Lord, for
we've been for - giv - en, and we've been re - stored. A -
mi - gos de Cris - to, we're friends of the Lord.

# Christ has Arisen

# All glory, laud, and honor

All glo - ry, laud, and hon - or to you, re - deem - er, king. To you the lips of chil - dren make sweet ho - san - nas ring.

1. The chil - dren of Je - ru - sa - lem with
2. The com - pa - ny of an - gels is

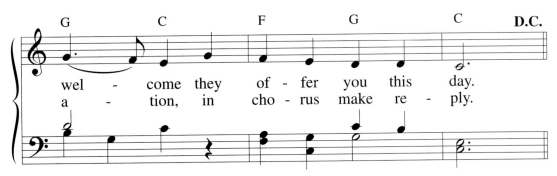

palms a-dorn your way. Their praise and prayer and
prais-ing you on high, Their and we, with all cre -

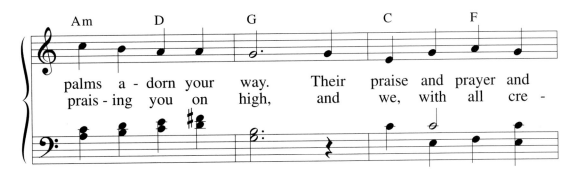

wel - come they of-fer you this day.
a - tion, in cho-rus make re-ply.

Words: *Gloria, laus et honor,* Theodulph of Orleans, c760-821; tr. John M. Neale, 1818-1866; adapt. by Nancy Roth, b. 1936, and eds., © 1997
Music: ST. THEODULPH, Melchior Teschner, 1584-1635

# Little gray donkey

**Refrain**

Lit-tle gray don-key, lit-tle gray don-key, lit-tle gray don-key,

ho!

**Verses** **Fine**

1. Do you know just who it is you
2. Once you were a sim - ple beast of
3. Yon - der is a grass - y hill; it's

car - ry on your back? 'Tis no or - di -
poor and low - ly state. Christ him - self has
known as Cal - va - ry. Up a - gainst the

nar - y load, no mean or com - mon pack.
cho - sen you and hon - ored is your fate.
cloud - less sky a bar - ren cross you see.

Verse lyrics:

1. You___ are bless - ed of___ all beasts to car - ry in - to town Christ the Lord of Gal - i - lee; he wears no earth - ly crown.

2. Though___ your path with palms___ is spread, make haste a - long the way; you were des - tined here to ride on this tri - um - phal day.

3. Lit - tle gray don - key, lit - tle gray mare, don't hide your head in shame. For you bear the lamb of God, and Je - sus is his name.

Words and music: Natalie Sleeth, 1930-1992, alt., © The Choristers Guild. Used by permission.

# Were you there?

F      C7      F

1. Were you there when they cru - ci - fied my Lord? Were you
2. Were you there when they nailed him to the tree? Were you
3. Were you there when they laid him in the tomb? Were you
4. Were you there when he rose up from the dead? Were you

Bb      F      C

there when they cru - ci - fied my Lord?
there when they nailed him to the tree?
there when they laid him in the tomb?
there when he rose up from the dead?

F Bb     F      Bb F      Am      Dm

O!            Some - times it caus - es me to

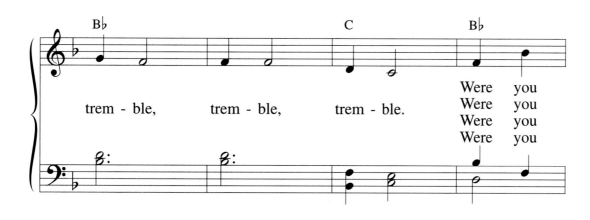

Bb                                  C              Bb

trem - ble,        trem - ble,        trem - ble.

Were    you
Were    you
Were    you
Were    you

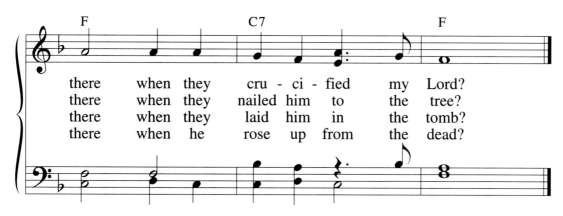

F                          C7                    F

there    when    they    cru - ci - fied    my    Lord?
there    when    they    nailed    him    to    the    tree?
there    when    they    laid    him    in    the    tomb?
there    when    he    rose    up    from    the    dead?

Words and music: WERE YOU THERE, African-American traditional

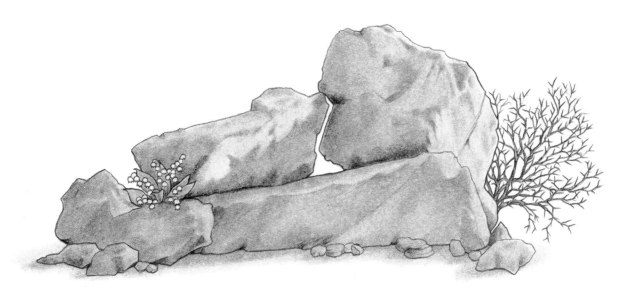

# Christ has arisen

1. Christ has a - ris - en, al - le - lu - ia!
2. Je - sus is liv - ing, let the earth sing.

Re - joice and praise him, al - le - lu - ia,
He reigns tri - um - phant, e - ter - nal king,

for our re - deem - er burst from the tomb,
and he has prom - ised those who be - lieve

e - ven from death, dis - pel - ling its gloom.
in - to his king - dom he will re - ceive.

Rhythm instrument pattern:

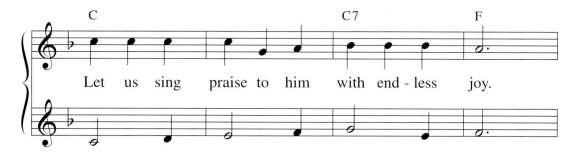

Let us sing praise to him with end-less joy.

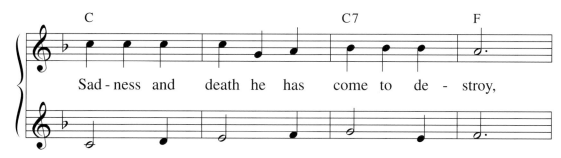

Sad-ness and death he has come to de - stroy,

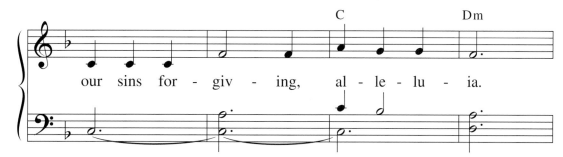

our sins for - giv - ing, al - le - lu - ia.

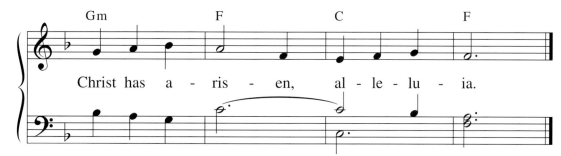

Christ has a - ris - en, al - le - lu - ia.

Words: Bernard Kyamanywa (Swahili); tr. Howard S. Olson, 1969, alt.
Music: HE HAS ARISEN, ALLELUIA, Haya traditional (Tanzania)
© 1977, Lutheran World Federation

# We welcome glad Easter

71

1. We welcome glad Easter when Jesus our Lord a-
2. And tell how three Marys came early that day, and
3. And sing of the angel who said: "Do not fear! Your

rose from the dead and will live evermore.
found at the dark tomb the stone rolled away. Then
savior is risen and he is not here."

raise joyful voices, all children, and sing. Bring

glad Easter praises to Jesus, our king.

Words: Unknown
Music: ST. DENIO, Welsh traditional; arr. Janette Cooper, b. 1937, alt., © 1987, Oxford University Press

# O how good is Christ the Lord 72

O how good is Christ the Lord! On the cross he died for me.

In three days he rose a-gain. Glo-ry be to Je - sus!

Glo-ry be to Je - sus! Glo-ry be to Je - sus!

In three days he rose a-gain. Glo-ry be to Je - sus!

Words: Puerto Rican traditional
Music: OH QUE BUENO ES JESUS, Puerto Rican traditional

# Gloria

**Round**

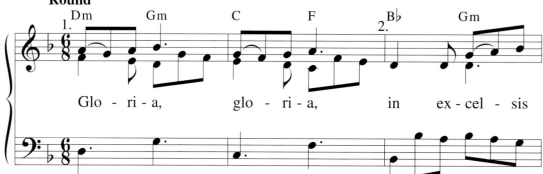

Glo - ri - a,  glo - ri - a,  in  ex - cel - sis

De - o!  Glo - ri - a,  glo - ri - a,

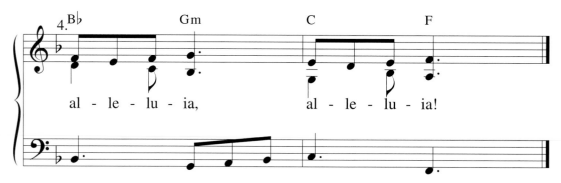

al - le - lu - ia,  al - le - lu - ia!

Music: GLORIA, Jacques Berthier, 1923-1994, © 1979, 1988, Les Presses de Taizé, GIA Publications, Inc. agent

# That Easter day

1. That East-er day with joy was bright. The
2. When to the tomb the wom-en came, they
3. Dear Lord, we thank you for that day, which

sun shone out with fair-er light, when, sent by God to
saw the an-gel bright as flame. "Fear not," he said, "your
gave us hope, for which we pray, that, at the end of

Je-sus' tomb, an an-gel rolled a-way the stone.
Lord you'll see if you go on to Gal-i-lee."
our last breath, there's life with you in-stead of death.

Words: St. 1, Latin, 5th cent., tr. John M. Neale, 1818-1866, alt..; st. 2-3, Nancy Roth, b. 1936, © 1997
Music: PUER NOBIS NASCITUR, *Christliche Gesangbüchlein,* 1568; adapt. by Michael Praetorius, 1571-1621

Christ our Lord is ris - en. Christ our Lord is ris - en.

Christ our Lord is ris - en and lives for - ev - er - more, and

lives for - ev - er - more, and lives for - ev - er - more.

Christ our Lord is ris - en and lives for - ev - er - more.

Words: Norman Carleton Mealy, 1923-1987, and Margaret W. Mealy, b. 1922, © 1961, Seabury Press
Music: American traditional; harm. from *Sing for joy,* © 1961,
    Seabury Press

# O sons and daughters, let us sing

1. O sons and daugh-ters, let us sing!
2. On this most ho-ly day of days,

The king of heav'n, the glo-rious king,
to God your hearts and voic-es raise

o'er death to-day rose tri-umph-ing.
in laud, and ju-bi-lee, and praise.

Al-le-lu-ia, al-le-lu-ia, al-le-lu-ia!
Al-le-lu-ia, al-le-lu-ia, al-le-lu-ia!

Words: Jean Tisserand, d. 1494, *O filii et filiae;* tr. John M. Neale, 1818-1866, *Medieval Hymns and Sequences,* 1851; alt. by compilers of *Hymns Ancient and Modern,* 1861
Music: GELOBT SEI GOTT, Melchior Vulpius, c1550-1615, *Ein schön geistlich Gesangbuch*

# Songs
## of Peace

# Dona nobis pacem

**Round**

Do - na no - bis pa - cem, pa - cem.

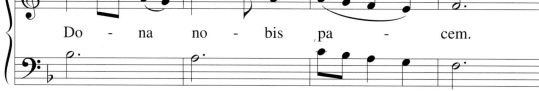

Do - na no - bis pa - cem.

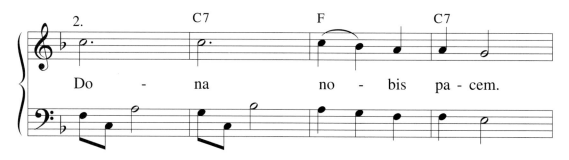

Do - na no - bis pa - cem.

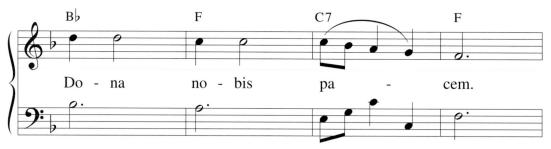

Do - na no - bis pa - cem.

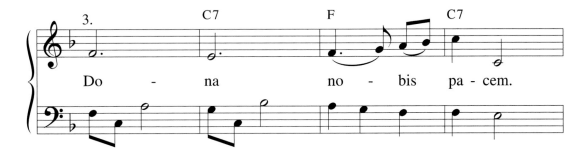

Do - na        no - bis  pa - cem.

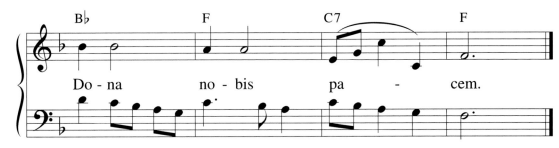

Do - na        no - bis    pa -      cem.

Words and music: DONA NOBIS PACEM, traditional

# Peace is flowing like a river

1. Peace is flow-ing like a riv - er,
2. Joy is flow-ing like a riv - er,
3. Love is flow-ing like a riv - er,

flow-ing out through you and me, flow-ing out in-to the

des - ert, set - ting all the cap-tives free.

Words and music: PEACE IS FLOWING, unknown

# In Christ there is no east or west

1. In Christ there is no east or west, in
2. Join hands, dis - ci - ples of the faith, what-
3. In Christ now meet both east and west, in

him no south or north, but one great fam - 'ly
e'er your race may be. Who serve each oth - er
him meet south and north. All Christ - ly souls are

bound by love through - out the whole wide earth.
in Christ's love are sure - ly kin to me.
one in him, through - out the whole wide earth.

Words: Based on Galatians 3:26-28; John Oxenham, 1852-1941
Music: MC KEE, African-American traditional; adapt. by Harry T. Burleigh, 1866-1949

# God's children speak in diff'rent tongues  80

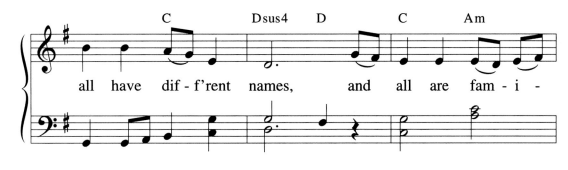

all have dif-f'rent names, and all are fam-i-

ly to me, and God loves us the same.

Words: Nancy Byrd Turner, 1880-1971, alt., © 1924, Sydney A. Weston
Music: KINGSFOLD, English traditional

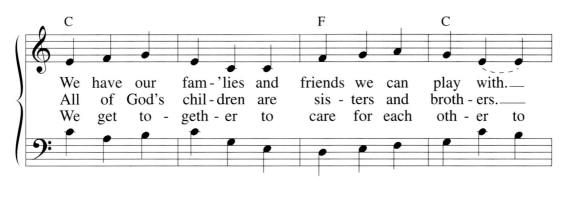

We have our fam-'lies and friends we can play with.___
All of God's chil-dren are sis-ters and broth-ers.___
We get to-geth-er to care for each oth-er to

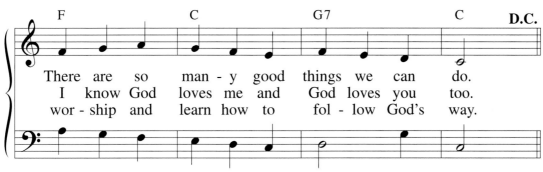

There are so man-y good things we can do.
I know God loves me and God loves you too.
wor-ship and learn how to fol-low God's way.

D.C.

Words and music: Patricia Joyce Shelly, b. 1951, alt., © 1977

# Shalom, my friends

**Round**

1. Sha - lom, my — friends, sha - lom, my — friends, sha - lom, sha - lom. Sha - lom, my — friends, sha - lom, my — friends, sha - lom, sha - lom.
2. Sha - lom, my — friends, sha - lom, my — friends, sha - lom, sha - lom. God's peace be with you. God's peace be with you, sha - lom, sha - lom.
3. *Sha - lom cha - ve - rim, sha - lom cha - ve - rim, sha - lom, sha - lom. Le - hit - ra - ot, le - hit - ra - ot, sha - lom, sha - lom.*

Words: Israeli traditional; tr. Theodore Wuerffel, b. 1944, ©
Music: SHALOM, Israeli traditional

# Go now in peace

**Round**

Go now in peace. Go now in peace. May the love of

God sur - round you ev - 'ry - where,

ev - 'ry - where you may go.

Words and music: GO NOW IN PEACE, Natalie Sleeth, 1930-1992, © 1976, Hinshaw Music, Inc. Printed with permission.

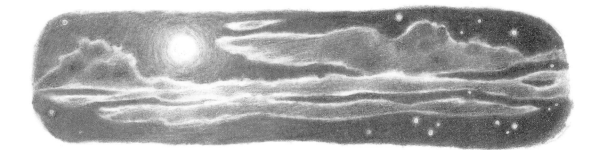

# Thinking
## about Heaven

*Chat-ter with the an - gels soon in the morn - ing.

Chat-ter with the an-gels in that land. Chat-ter with the an-gels

soon in the morn-ing. Chat-ter with the an-gels, join the band.

I hope to join that band and chat-ter with the an-gels

*March* with the angels
*Skip* with the angels
*Dance* with the angels
*Tiptoe* with the angels

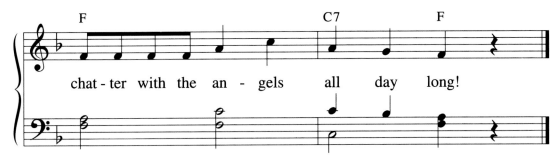

all day long! I hope to join that band and

chat - ter with the an - gels all day long!

Words and music: African-American traditional

# 'Tis a gift to be simple

'Tis a gift to be sim-ple. 'Tis a gift to be free. 'Tis a

gift to come down where we ought to be, and

when we find our-selves in the place just right, 'twill

be in the val-ley of love and de-light.

When true sim-plic-i-ty is gained, to bow and to bend we
shan't be a-shamed. To turn, turn, will be our de-light till by
turn-ing, turn-ing, we come round right.

Words and music: SIMPLE GIFTS, Shaker traditional, 19th cent.

shore, al - le - lu - ia. Mich-ael, row___ the boat a -
sail, al - le - lu - ia. Sis - ter, help___ to trim the
wide, al - le - lu - ia. Milk and hon-ey on the oth - er
shore, al - le - lu - ia. Mich-ael, row___ the boat a -

shore, al - le - lu - ia.
sail, al - le - lu - ia.
side, al - le - lu - ia.
shore, al - le - lu - ia.

1. Mich - ael, row the boat a -
2. Sis - ter, help to trim the
3. Jor - dan's riv - er's deep and
4. Mich - ael, row the boat a -

Words and music: African-American traditional

# God loves many diff'rent people  87

1. God loves man-y diff'rent peo-ple with sur-pass-ing
2. God wants you to come a-long now, wants you as a

love, bless-es all the man-y chil-dren,
child. Come, my friend, O come a-long now.

cares for ev-'ry one. Come a-long, friend,
God loves ev-'ry one.

come a-long, friend, come, re-ceive God's joy.

Earth-ly things don't last for-ev-er, come, re-ceive God's joy.

Words: Lubunda Mukungu; tr. rev. Anna Juhnke, alt.
Music: Tshiluba traditional (Zaire)
© 1978, Mennonite World Conference

# Shall we gather at the river

1. Shall we gath-er at the riv - er,
2. On the mar-gin of the riv - er,

where bright an-gel feet have trod,
wash - ing up its sil - ver spray,

with its crys-tal tide for-
we will walk and wor-ship

ev - er flow-ing by the throne of God?
ev - er, all the hap-py gold - en day.

Yes, we'll gath-er at the riv - er, the beau-ti-ful, the beau-ti-ful

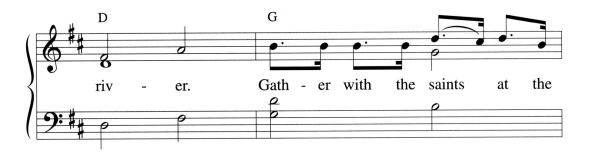

river. Gath - er with the saints at the

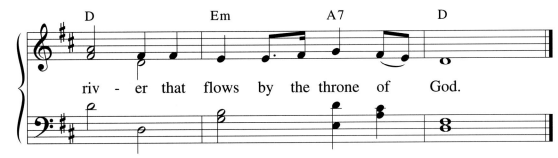

riv - er that flows by the throne of God.

Words and music: BEAUTIFUL RIVER, Robert Lowry, 1826-1899

# Hop up and jump up

Hop up and jump up and whirl 'round, whirl 'round.

Gath-er love, here it is, all 'round, all 'round.

Here is love, flow-ing 'round. Catch it as you whirl 'round.

Reach up and reach down. Here it is, all 'round.

Words and music: Shaker traditional

# At the gates of heav'n

1. At the gates of heav'n ti - ny shoes they are giv - ing
2. An - gel choirs in heav'n with their voic - es are bring - ing

to the lit - tle bare - foot - ed an - gels there liv - ing.
joy - ous songs of love all for you they are sing - ing.

Slum - ber my lit - tle one. Slum - ber my lit - tle one.

Slum - ber my ni - ño, a - rru, a - rru.

# Subject Index

# Types of Songs

Lullabies  31, 40, 42, 45, 52, 53, 54, 90
Rounds and canons  13, 25, 27, 30, 60, 65, 73, 77, 82, 83
Table graces  13, 24, 25, 27, 28

# Tune Index

# Index of Authors, Translators, and Sources

# Index of Composers, Arrangers, and Sources

# Index of First Lines